AIR DISASTERS

MICHAEL WOODS AND MARY B WOODS

LERNER BOOKS • LONDON • NEW YORK • MINNEAPOLIS

To St Bonaventure University,
for our smooth take-off

Editor's note: Determining the exact death toll following disasters is often difficult—if not impossible—especially in the case of disasters that took place long ago. The authors and the editors in this series have used their best judgement in determining which figures to include.

First published in the United Kingdom in 2010 by
Lerner Books,
Dalton House,
60 Windsor Avenue,
London SW19 2RR

Website address: www.lernerbooks.co.uk

This edition was updated and edited for UK publication by Discovery Books Ltd.,
First Floor, 2 College Street, Ludlow, Shropshire SY8 1AN

British Library Cataloguing in Publication Data
   Woods, Michael, 1943-
   Air disasters. - 2nd ed. - (Disasters up close)
   1. Aircraft accidents - Juvenile literature
   I. Title II. Woods, Mary B. (Mary Boyle), 1946--
363.1'24

ISBN-13: 978 0 7613 4403 2

Printed in China

Contents

INTRODUCTION   4

What Is an Air Disaster?   6

Recipe for Disaster   14

Disaster Danger Zones   26

Measuring the Menace   32

Getting Help — FAST   40

The Future   50

TIMELINE   56

GLOSSARY   58

PLACES TO VISIT   59

SOURCE NOTES   59

SELECTED BIBLIOGRAPHY   61

FURTHER RESOURCES   61

INDEX   63

Introduction

ON 12 NOVEMBER 2001, AMERICAN AIRLINES FLIGHT 587 WAS SET TO TAKE OFF FROM JOHN F KENNEDY INTERNATIONAL AIRPORT IN NEW YORK CITY, USA. THE PILOTS EXPECTED IT TO BE A BUMPY RIDE. A BIG BOEING 747, A JUMBO JET, HAD JUST TAKEN OFF IN FRONT OF THEM. ON TAKE-OFF, BIG PLANES CHURN UP THE AIR. THEIR WINGS CREATE WHIRLWINDS, ALMOST LIKE MINI TORNADOES. THE ROUGH AIR IS CALLED WAKE TURBULENCE. IT CAN SHAKE UP PLANES LIKE A FIZZY DRINK. BUT PILOT ED STATES AND CO-PILOT STEN MOLIN WERE NOT WORRIED. THEY WERE TRAINED TO FLY SAFELY THROUGH WAKE TURBULENCE.

Sixty-six seconds after take-off, Flight 587 hit the choppy air. Ed States spoke to air traffic controllers through his radio. 'Wake encounter,' he said. Then a strange rattling sound filled the cockpit. The pilots heard a bump and another rattle. Then the plane's tail fin ripped off.

Without a tail fin, an aeroplane can't fly. It will spin around and fall from the sky. That's what happened to Flight 587. It spun to the ground. It crashed into homes and buildings in Rockaway Beach, New York.

BALL OF FIRE

The aeroplane carried thousands of litres of jet fuel. When the plane hit the ground, the fuel splattered everywhere, like water from a water balloon. The fuel exploded, burned and set fire to houses. Pat Gray lived near the crash site. 'I heard an explosion,' she said. 'The TV went off and I went to the front door and the whole street was engulfed in black smoke.'

Close to the crash site, Angela Spencer saw the plane come down. 'I was looking out of the back window,' she said. 'There were pieces coming off [the plane] and it turned into a big ball of fire and smoke. People were running up the road and the children were screaming.'

Kevin McKeon first heard the explosion. Then 'we felt this shudder and the room just exploded', McKeon said. 'My daughter got blown through the patio doors. My wife got blown into the living room. And I got blown out the patio doors behind my daughter.'

LOST IN THE WRECKAGE

Pieces of the aeroplane hit buildings and people on the ground. One of the plane's huge engines landed in a petrol station car park. All the passengers on board – 260 people – died in the crash. Five people on the ground died. Victims' bodies were scattered everywhere. Their suitcases and clothing were scattered around the wreckage.

When people heard about a plane crash on TV and radio, they all wondered one thing: were their family members or friends on *that* plane?

The rubble of Flight 587 mixes with pieces of homes damaged by the impact in Rockaway Beach, New York.

What Is an Air Disaster?

LIKE ALL DISASTERS, AIR DISASTERS ARE BIG, TRAGIC EVENTS. LARGE NUMBERS OF PEOPLE ARE HURT. THEY OFTEN DAMAGE OR DESTROY BUILDINGS. AIR DISASTERS INVOLVE AIRCRAFT. AEROPLANES ARE THE MOST COMMON TYPE OF AIRCRAFT AND AN AEROPLANE CRASH IS THE MOST COMMON TYPE OF AIR DISASTER.

BIG DISASTERS

Most air disasters involve big passenger aeroplanes. Big planes can carry hundreds of people. For instance, a Boeing 747 can hold about 420 people. The Airbus A380 can carry more than 500 people. When a big plane crashes, the death toll can be huge.

The worst air disaster in history took place on 11 September 2001. On that day, terrorists took over four passenger aeroplanes in the United States. The terrorists crashed two of the planes into the World Trade Center towers in New York City. A third plane hit the Pentagon, US military headquarters near Washington, DC. The fourth plane crashed in a field in Pennsylvania. The crashes killed thousands of people in the buildings that got hit. Everyone in the aeroplanes died too. In total, more than three thousand people died in the 11 September attacks.

The Airbus A380 is the world's largest commercial airliner.

United Airlines Flight 175 flies towards the south
tower of the World Trade Center on 11 September
2001. The hijacked plane crashed into the tower,
causing it to collapse later in the day.

HARD-TO-TELL DISASTERS

Some disasters are easy to predict. For instance, scientists know that every year, dozens of hurricanes will form in the Atlantic Ocean. Some of these storms will hit land. They might damage buildings and hurt people. When people know a hurricane is coming, they can take steps to protect their homes. They can even leave the area. Nobody knows, however, when an air disaster is coming. Most air disasters are accidents. Accidents happen suddenly, without warning.

AEROPLANE SAFETY

Some people are afraid to fly in aeroplanes. They worry that their plane might crash. The truth is that flying is one of the safest ways to travel. It is much safer than travelling by car. The odds of dying in an aeroplane crash are approximately 1 in 10 million. However, your chances of dying in a car crash this year are 1 in 8,000. Only a handful of UK citizens die in air accidents each year, many in small, private planes. By comparison, over 3,000 people are killed each year on Britain's roads.

RISKY THINKING

Air travel seems dangerous to many people. That's because it's unfamiliar. Most people don't fly in aeroplanes every day, so the occasional trip can feel scary. Everyday activities, such as driving a car, are more familiar. Therefore, they feel safer. People also feel safer when they control a situation. For instance, drivers feel safe in cars, knowing that they control them. Aeroplane passengers don't have this feeling of control.

Pan Am Flight 103 created this crater in Lockerbie, Scotland, when it crashed after being bombed in 1988. While an air accident can cause more deaths at one time, car accidents still cause more deaths overall.

Modern aeroplanes are built to be safe. They have emergency exits, seatbelts and many other safety devices. Aeroplane pilots receive top-level training. A government agency called the Civil Aviation Authority oversees aeroplane travel in the United Kingdom. It makes sure that air travel is as safe as possible.

Since passenger flights began, air travel has become safer and safer. Still, flying in aeroplanes will never be 100 per cent safe. The skies are crowded with aircraft. Every day in the United States, for example, about eighty-seven thousand aeroplanes take to the air. With so many planes in flight, there's always a risk that one will crash.

THE FIRST CRASH VICTIM

Orville and Wilbur Wright built the first successful aeroplane. They made their first flight at Kitty Hawk, North Carolina, USA, in 1903. Five years later, in 1908, Thomas Selfridge was flying with Orville Wright at Fort Myer, Virginia. Their plane crashed *(below)*. Selfridge was killed and Wright was badly injured. Selfridge was the first person ever killed in an aeroplane crash.

'There was this **thunderous explosion**, and *I was startled*, because there was a **great big jolt**, and *I looked up. My hair was flowing* into the sky and just above me were clouds.'

– *a passenger on Aloha Airlines Flight 243 in 1988, after the ceiling of the plane was ripped off*

Aeroplanes line up to take off at one of the busiest airports in the world, Chicago's O'Hare International Airport.

The *Hindenburg* catches fire as it lands in New Jersey.

1937
THE HINDENBERG

An airship is an unusual kind of aircraft. It looks like a huge, long, thin balloon. Part of the craft is filled with a gas which is lighter than air. This gas makes the airship float in the sky. Engines and propellers move the airship through the air. Airships are also called blimps or dirigibles.

In the 1930s, airships were a popular way to travel. At the time, aeroplanes were small. They could not fly far, but airships could fly across a whole country – or a whole ocean – without stopping. For passengers, riding in an airship was like staying in a luxury hotel. Passengers had their own rooms. A dining room served delicious meals.

The *Hindenburg* was the largest and most famous airship. Built in Germany, the *Hindenburg* was 245 metres long. That's almost as long as two and a half football pitches. The *Hindenburg* could carry about one hundred passengers and crew members. It could fly nearly 13,000 kilometres (8,000 miles) without stopping. Flying on the *Hindenburg* felt like being **'carried in the arms of angels,'** according to one passenger.

In May 1937, the *Hindenburg* crossed the Atlantic Ocean from

Europe to the United States. On 6 May, it was set to land in New Jersey. On board were ninety-seven passengers and crew members. Hundreds of people had gathered on the ground. Some were meeting family or friends returning from Europe. Others just wanted to see the famous airship.

Radio announcer Herbert Morrison reported on the *Hindenburg*'s arrival. **'Here it comes, ladies and gentlemen,'** Morrison said. '**And what a sight it is, a thrilling one, a marvellous sight. . . . The sun is striking the windows of the observation deck on the westward side.'**

Suddenly, there was a tremendous explosion. The gas inside the *Hindenburg* caught on fire. The airship burst into flames. **'Oh . . . oh . . . oh,'** Morrison said. **'It's burst into flames . . . get out of the way please! It's burning, bursting into flames and is falling.'**

Newspaper photographer Murray Becker was another eyewitness. **'The ship burst towards the tail end,'** Becker remembered. **'The tail went down first and the nose seemed to hang in the air. In a fraction of a second there was nothing left but the skeleton.'**

Amazingly, the crash killed only thirty-five passengers and one person on the ground. After the disaster, people were afraid to ride in airships. Passenger flights on airships ended.

However, people still use airships for advertising, aerial observation, photographing certain sporting events, and carrying cargo.

The *Hindenburg* took less than one minute to become completely engulfed in flames.

Recipe for Disaster

ON 15 APRIL 2002, AIR CHINA FLIGHT 129 WAS ABOUT TO LAND AT AN AIRPORT IN SOUTH KOREA, BUT THE PILOT AND CO-PILOT STRUGGLED WITH THE WEATHER. STRONG WINDS MADE IT HARD FOR THEM TO CONTROL THE PLANE. HEAVY FOG AND RAIN MADE IT HARD TO SEE. THEN THE PILOTS MADE A MISTAKE. CONFUSED BY THE BAD WEATHER, THEY DIDN'T TURN THE PLANE TOWARDS THE RUNWAY AS PLANNED. THEY MISTAKENLY FLEW THE PLANE STRAIGHT INTO A 300-M HILL. THE PLANE CRASHED INTO THE HILLSIDE. OF THE 166 PEOPLE ON BOARD, 128 DIED. MANY OF THE SURVIVORS WERE BADLY HURT.

The Air China accident involved the two main causes of air disasters: mistakes by pilots and bad weather. Terrorism – violent acts such as bombing – is a less common cause of air disasters.

TO ERR IS HUMAN

Flying a plane takes experience and judgement. If problems arise in flight, pilots must make decisions quickly. Pilots who fly for big airlines are well trained. They have degrees and many years of experience flying planes. Some are former RAF pilots. They have flown fighter planes on dangerous missions. Yet pilots aren't perfect. They can make mistakes. In fact, pilot error is the number one cause of air disasters.

This pilot sits in the cockpit of a Boeing 747. Pilots must train for years before they can fly large passenger planes.

The wreckage of Air China Flight 129
burns on a hillside.

In addition to pilots, many other people help aeroplanes fly. Air traffic controllers keep track of hundreds of aeroplanes. They use radar to monitor the planes in the sky. They also use computers and other tracking systems. They make sure that aeroplanes in flight stay a safe distance from one another. They tell pilots when it is safe to travel down runways, take off and land. However, air traffic controllers are human too. They can also make mistakes, such as misreading a radar screen.

Other workers repair and maintain aeroplanes, pump fuel into planes and load baggage. These workers, too, can make mistakes. For instance, in 1979 airport workers entered the wrong instructions into the computer on board Air New Zealand Flight 901. The plane took passengers on a sightseeing flight over Antarctica. The computer error made the plane fly in the wrong direction. The pilots didn't realize that they were going the wrong way because they were flying through heavy clouds, which blocked their view. By the time they realized something was wrong, it was too late. The plane crashed into a mountain, killing all 257 people on board.

An aircraft mechanic works on a jet engine from a 747 cargo plane. Many people work to ensure the safety of every aeroplane.

These air traffic
controllers are using
radar screens to direct
air and runway traffic.

WEATHER OR NOT

Bad weather is the second most common cause of air disasters. Usually, pilots can avoid bad weather. Modern aeroplanes often fly more than 10,000 m) above the ground. At this height, they fly *above* most bad weather.

Aeroplanes also have radar screens. These devices show pilots the location of rain and snow. Pilots can change a plane's course to avoid bad weather they see on their radar screens. They can fly higher to get above the weather or steer around a storm.

Sometimes, however, it's impossible to avoid bad weather. For instance, during take-offs and landings, planes fly low in the sky, where there might be storms. Sometimes, bad weather hits unexpectedly. Then pilots and air traffic controllers must make quick decisions: Should planes on the ground take off? Should planes in the air land, or should they circle in the sky until the bad weather clears? Should they fly to another airport where the weather is better? Sometimes, pilots and controllers don't make the right decisions. In the air transport business, bad decisions can be deadly.

SNOW AND ICE, BURSTS AND BUMPS

During winter, snow and ice might cover airport runways. Icy runways are slippery and dangerous, just like icy roads. And just like car drivers, pilots might have trouble steering and stopping aeroplanes on ice- and snow-covered runways. Airport workers use ploughs to keep runways clear, but sometimes snow piles up faster than ploughs can clear it.

In 2005 a snowstorm hit Chicago. Southwest Airlines Flight 1248 skidded on a snowy runway during landing. The aeroplane slid onto a busy road near the airport. It crashed into several cars. The crash killed one car passenger, a six-year-old boy. Several other car passengers were seriously injured.

AVOIDING BAD WEATHER IN FLIGHT

Jets cruise more than 10,000m above the ground.

During cold, rainy weather, pilots and airport workers worry about ice forming on aeroplane wings. Even a thin coating of ice can make the wing surface rough. Without smooth, ice-free wings, a plane cannot climb properly or stay in the air.

At airports, planes often sit outside during rainstorms and snowstorms. During these times, ice can build up on aeroplanes' wings. So workers at airports spray planes with de-icing liquid, a chemical that melts ice. Wings can also ice up during flight if a plane flies into freezing rain. The rain freezes instantly when it hits the plane's wings, coating them with ice. Modern planes have heaters that melt any ice on the wings.

A crew uses a chemical de-icing liquid to remove snow and ice from a plane following a blizzard in Denver, Colorado.

Even with heaters and de-icers, ice can still cause air disasters. In Washington, DC, USA, in 1982, Air Florida Flight 90 did not get a complete de-icing before take-off. The ice disrupted the flow of air that normally lifts a plane off the ground and keeps it in the sky. As a result, Flight 90 dropped out of the sky and crashed. Seventy-nine people on board died. In 1994 American Eagle Flight 4184 crashed after flying into freezing rain. That crash killed sixty-eight people.

Microbursts are another weather danger for aeroplanes. These small, sudden, downward blasts of wind frequently occur during rainstorms. During take-offs and landings, microbursts can hit planes without warning and knock them to the ground.

Air turbulence – or bumpy air – can hit an aeroplane that is flying high. Turbulence often occurs without warning – even when the sky ahead is clear. Turbulence rarely causes crashes, but it can shake an aeroplane and damage it. Passengers who are not wearing seatbelts might bounce around and get hurt.

Workers remove the tail section of Air Florida Flight 90 from the Potomac River, near Washington, in 1982.

MECHANICAL FAILURE

Aeroplanes are built to stay in the air. For instance, most passenger planes have more than one engine. If one engine fails, the plane can still keep flying with another engine. In addition, mechanics and other workers spend many hours inspecting, maintaining and fixing aeroplanes to keep them in top condition.

BELIEVE IT OR NOT

How could a 500-gram bird destroy a 40-tonne aeroplane? By flying into the aeroplane's engines, that's how. In 1988 an Ethiopian Airlines flight took off into the sky. Immediately after take-off, the plane's powerful engines sucked in some pigeons. The birds damaged the engines. The plane crashed. Thirty-one people died.

Aeroplanes are still machines. They have engines, landing gear and other mechanical equipment. Even with the best maintenance, mechanical equipment can wear out or break down. In July 1996, 230 people died when Trans World Airlines (TWA) Flight 800 crashed into the Atlantic Ocean. Investigators determined that the cause was a short circuit in the plane's electrical wiring system. The short circuit caused the plane's fuel tank to explode.

The remains of TWA Flight 800 sit in a US Navy
hangar. Investigators put the pieces back together
to determine the cause of the crash – a short
circuit in the electrical wiring.

Two men from a rescue party look at the remains of the two aeroplanes that crashed into the Grand Canyon in 1956.

1956
THE GRAND CANYON

On 30 June 1956, two aeroplanes left Los Angeles airport just after nine in the morning. United Airlines Flight 718 was taking fifty-eight people from Los Angeles to Chicago. TWA Flight 2 was carrying seventy people from Los Angeles to Kansas City.

Both planes were following flight plans. According to the plans, United 718 would fly at 6,400 m above the ground. TWA 2 would fly at 5,800 m above the ground. The planes would cross paths at about 10.30 am. The crossing would happen over the Painted Desert – a beautiful area on the edge of the Grand Canyon in Arizona. There seemed to be no danger. According to the flight plans,

United 718 would fly 610 m above TWA 2.

In the 1950s, air traffic control was very basic. Controllers did not use radar and computers to track aeroplanes in flight. Once the two planes left Los Angeles, nobody watched to make sure they stayed a safe distance apart. The pilots had only radios to communicate with the airline headquarters.

Captain Jack Gandy, pilot of TWA 2, saw thunderstorms forming above the Grand Canyon. Gandy radioed TWA headquarters. He asked to climb above the storm, to 6,400 m. TWA asked the Los Angeles control tower about Gandy's request. The tower said no – because United 718 was already flying at 6,400 m . So Gandy asked permission to fly higher than 6,400 m . He promised to watch out for United 718. The control tower approved the request.

Nobody is sure what happened next. Most likely, both pilots were flying a little off their planned courses. They probably wanted to give passengers a better view of the Grand

An army helicopter hovers over the site of the 1956 plane crash in the Grand Canyon.

Canyon. In any event, at 10.31 am the planes crashed into each other at 6,400 m. The pilots in the TWA plane probably never saw United 718, because it approached from behind. United 718's left wing hit the top of the TWA plane. Its propellers sliced open TWA 2 like a knife.

Captain Robert Shirley, pilot of United 718, radioed a message to the control tower at the airport in Salt Lake City, Utah. He said his plane was going down. Both planes crashed into the Grand Canyon. All 128 people died.

'Salt Lake, United 718 . . . uh . . . we're going in.'

– Captain Robert Shirley

Disaster Danger Zones

EARTHQUAKES AND HURRICANES ONLY HAPPEN IN CERTAIN PARTS OF THE WORLD. OTHER DISASTERS, SUCH AS BLIZZARDS AND TORNADOES, USUALLY HAPPEN AT CERTAIN TIMES OF THE YEAR. AIR DISASTERS ARE DIFFERENT. AIR DISASTERS CAN HAPPEN AT ANY TIME OF THE YEAR. AND AEROPLANES CAN CRASH ANYWHERE.

However, wealthy countries, have more money to spend on airline safety. Other countries, such as developing countries in Asia and Africa, have less money for airline safety. As a result, air disasters are more likely to happen in poor countries than in wealthy ones.

SAFE IN THE SKY

Every aeroplane flight includes three main stages: take-off, cruising and landing. Cruising is the safest part of the flight.

Aeroplanes usually cruise at 10,668 m in the air. Suppose an aeroplane encounters a problem, such as mechanical failure, during cruising. The pilots would certainly be worried, but they would also have time to solve the problem. An aeroplane can glide, or descend, gradually, even if its engines have stopped running. Gliding high in the sky, the pilots could find a solution to their problem. They wouldn't have to worry about hitting the ground immediately.

UPWARD DISASTERS

Take-off is a dangerous time for aeroplanes. During take-off, the aeroplane is at its heaviest. It is loaded with fuel for the flight ahead. A Boeing 747 might weigh about

FAST FACT
A Boeing 747 can carry nearly 216,000 litres of fuel. That's enough fuel to fill a big swimming pool.

408,000 kg at the beginning of a flight. The fuel can account for more than half that weight.

To get the heavy plane into the air, the plane's engines must work at full power. Sometimes, an engine or another mechanical part breaks under the stress. In addition, bad weather occurs close to the ground. Planes sometimes fly into storms immediately after take-off.

Suppose an aeroplane encounters a problem soon after take-off. The plane is near the ground. It can't glide through the air for many minutes as it can during cruising. The pilots have just seconds to solve the problem. If they don't solve it quickly, the plane might crash to the ground.

DOWNWARD DISASTERS

Other air disasters often happen at the end of a flight – during the landing phase. Landings can be dangerous for several reason.

One reason is low altitude (height above the ground). As with take-offs, the closer an aeroplane is to the ground, the less time a pilot has to react to a problem, be it a microburst, thunderstorm or mechanical failure.

Another factor is speed. Aeroplanes must slow down to land safely. By the time a Boeing 747 lands, it will have slowed to about 160 km (100 miles) per hour. But aeroplanes need speed to stay airborne. The slower an aeroplane's speed, the harder it is for pilots to control.

South-west Airlines Flight 1445 skidded off the end of a runway at the Burbank, California, airport in 2000.

'*The runway lights were gone and the concrete runway was coming to an end!*'

– Parker Moon, a passenger on Southwest Airlines Flight 1445, which crashed in California in 2000

FAMOUS AIR DISASTERS

Air disasters happen all around the world. This map shows just a few places where major air disasters have occurred.

LOCKERBIE (Scotland)
21 December, 1988
Pan Am 103
(270 deaths)

SENLIS (France)
3 March 1974
Turkish Airlines 981
(346 deaths)

SEA OF JAPAN –
1983,
Korean Airlines 007

PUSAN (South Korea)
15 April 2002
Air China 129
(128 deaths)

EUROPE

ASIA

BLACK SEA
3 May 2006
Armavia Airlines 967
(113 deaths)

PARIS (France)
25 July 2000
Concorde (113 deaths)

GUMMA PREFECTURE
(Japan)
12 August 1985
Japan Airlines 123
(520 deaths)

AFRICA

NEW DELHI (India)
12 November 1996
Saudi Arabian Airlines 763
Air Kazakhstan 1907
(351 deaths)

AUSTRALIA

CANARY ISLANDS (Spain)
March 27, 1977
KLM 4805 and Pan Am 736
(583 deaths)

NEW YORK CITY, NY (USA)
11 September 2001
American Airlines 11 and
United Airlines 175
(approximately 2,750 deaths)

ATLANTIC OCEAN (Canada)
2 September 1998
Swissair 111
(229 deaths)

ATLANTIC OCEAN (USA)
17 July 1996
TWA 800
(230 deaths)

NORTH AMERICA

GRAND CANYON, AZ (USA)
30 June 1956
United 718 and TWA 2
(128 deaths)

ARLINGTON, VA (USA)
11 September 2001
American Airlines 77
(189 deaths)

CHICAGO, ILLINOIS (USA)
25 May 1979
American Airlines 191
(273 deaths)

LAKEHURST, NJ (USA)
6 May 1937
Hindenburg
(36 deaths)

SOMERSET COUNTY, PA (USA)
11 September 2001
United Airlines 93
(44 deaths)

SOUTH AMERICA

MOUNT EREBUS (Antarctica)
November 28, 1979
Air New Zealand 901
(257 deaths)

Rescue workers search for survivors of Japan Airlines Flight 123 on a mountain in central Japan.

1985

JAPAN AIRLINES FLIGHT 123

In 1977 pilots for Japan Airlines (JAL) noticed an odd whistling noise when they flew a certain Boeing 747. The noise had started after workers repaired the plane's tail fin. Pilots heard the noise on and off for seven years. Nobody checked the plane to to find the problem. During that time, the aeroplane carried thousands of passengers on thousands of flights.

Nobody realized that the repairs to the tail fin had not been done properly years earlier. Nobody knew that the metal in the tail end of the plane was slowly getting weaker and weaker. Then, on 12 August 1985, everyone suddenly found out about the incomplete repairs.

At 6.12 PM, JAL Flight 123 took off from an airport in Tokyo. The plane carried 524 people: 509 passengers and 15 crew members. Twelve minutes after take-off, JAL 123 was 7,285 m above the ground. Its speed was 555 km (345 miles) per hour. Yumi Ochiai, a passenger,

Hey, there's a mountain. Turn right! Up! [Or] we'll crash into a mountain!

– Captain Masami Takahama, Japan Airlines Flight 123

remembered the first hint of the disaster ahead. **'There was a sudden loud noise,'** she said. **'It was somewhere to the right and overhead. It hurt my ears, and immediately the cabin filled with white mist.'**

In the cockpit, the pilot requested to return to the airport. The control tower approved the request. However, instead of returning to the airport, the plane started zig-zagging through the sky. A 5 m piece of tail fin had broken off the plane. The break occurred right where the faulty repairs had been made seven years earlier. With a broken tail fin, the pilots could not steer and control the aeroplane properly.

JAL 123 plunged to 2,000 m. Somehow, the pilots managed to keep the plane in the air for more than thirty minutes. That whole time, the passengers knew they were doomed. Some wrote good-bye letters to family and friends.

The plane turned towards high mountains. **'All of a sudden, a big aeroplane appeared from between the mountains, just like out of nowhere,'** said one eyewitness on the ground. **'Four times it leaned to the left, and each time it tried to recover its balance to the right.'**

A wing from Flight 123 landed on this hillside.

Another eyewitness described the scene: **'I was looking up in wonder when the aeroplane started to nosedive. Then there was a big crashing sound like a thunderbolt and then a flash, after which a mushroom cloud of smoke rose from behind the mountain.'**

Only 4 people survived the crash. 520 people died.

Measuring the Menace

WHEN PEOPLE HEAR ABOUT AN AIR DISASTER, THEY ASK QUESTIONS: HOW BAD WAS IT? HOW MANY PEOPLE WERE KILLED? WERE ANY OF MY FAMILY MEMBERS OR FRIENDS ON THAT PLANE?

Measuring air disasters does involve counting injuries and deaths, but there's more to the process than just that. After an air disaster, investigators try to find out why the aircraft crashed. They study the crash to learn how to prevent similar crashes in the future.

ACCIDENT DETECTIVES

The Air Accidents Investigation Branch (AAIB) is the government body that studies civil (non-military) aeroplane accidents in the UK.

Within hours of an air disaster, a team from the AAIB hurries to the scene. The team includes experts with many different jobs. Some experts interview eyewitnesses to the crash. Some examine weather conditions that might have caused the crash. Others sort through the wreckage of the aircraft. They look for signs of mechanical problems that could have caused the disaster. Still others look at radar images of the plane recorded just before the crash.

BLACK BOXES

Some of the first things investigators look for after a crash are the aeroplane's black boxes. These two recording devices are installed on all passenger planes.

MISSING BOXES

After some air disasters, black boxes are never found. Some sink into deep water. Some break apart during crashes, despite their protective steel coverings.

ENREGISTREUR
DE VOL
NE PAS
OUVRIR

The blackened remains of the data recorder from an aeroplane crash are shown below a new data recorder.

ENREGISTRE

NE PAS

OFFICIAL BUSINESS
UNITED STATES GOVERNMENT
NATIONAL TRANSPORTATION
SAFETY BOARD
ACCIDENT INVESTIGATION

One box is the plane's cockpit voice recorder (CVR). The other is the flight data recorder (FDR).

The CVR records all sounds heard inside the cockpit. It records conversations between the pilot and the co-pilot, announcements the pilots make to passengers and other sounds from the aeroplane. The FDR records other data about the aeroplane. This information includes the plane's speed, altitude, changes in direction and other movements. Investigators use the data from the black boxes to piece together information about a crash.

Often in an air disaster, all the plane's equipment is smashed to bits. However, the FDR and CVR are enclosed in strong steel boxes. The boxes protect the recordings from damage in a crash. The boxes can withstand hot flames from burning fuel. They can fall thousands of metres without breaking. The boxes are waterproof in case a plane crashes into a lake or ocean. Despite the nickname, black boxes are actually painted bright red or orange. The bright colour makes the boxes stand out among the other wreckage. It makes them easier to find.

WHY AND HOW?

After collecting all the information about a crash, experts from the AAIB begin an investigation. It is similar to the investigation that police officers use to solve a crime. AAIB workers look for

LIGHTBULB DISASTER

In 1972 Eastern Airlines Flight 401 was preparing to land at night at Miami International Airport. At the last minute, the pilot noticed a broken light bulb on the instrument panel. It should have been glowing to show that the landing gear was in the proper position for landing, but the bulb was dead. The pilot and co-pilot replaced the bulb. While doing so, they let the plane descend too quickly. The plane crashed in the Everglades region of Florida. The disaster killed 100 of 176 people on board. Investigators listened to recordings from the CVR to work out what had caused the crash. On the recordings, they heard the pilot and co-pilot talking about the lightbulb.

NTSB experts reconstructed this Boeing 747
that crashed into the Atlantic Ocean after taking
off from New York in 1996.

clues, such as broken machinery that might have caused the crash. By piecing all the clues together, investigators can usually find the cause of the disaster.

Some investigations are long and difficult. For instance, it took the American investigators four years to find out why TWA Flight 800 crashed into the Atlantic in 1996. Finally, investigators determined that an electrical short circuit had caused the crash.

Once the AAIB determines the cause of a crash, it uses this information to make air travel safer. For instance, if the AAIB finds that a faulty fuel tank caused a crash, it might require aeroplane manufacturers to improve fuel tanks.

THE HUMAN TRAGEDY

The cause of a crash is not the only mystery officials try to solve after an air disaster. Aeroplane crashes are violent. People who die in crashes often suffer severe burns and massive injuries. Their bodies may be impossible to recognize. It usually takes a team of experts to identify victims after a plane crash.

Specialist teams to identify air disaster victims. They include specially trained doctors and other medical workers. They may spend days or even weeks identifying victims at a crash scene.

Some air disaster victims can be identified quickly. For example, a body might be found intact with a purse or a wallet nearby. Investigators can compare a driver's licence photograph or other picture ID to the dead body.

Unfortunately many bodies are badly burned or torn up after air disasters. When this happens identification takes much longer. Investigators must do a lot of detective work. They often compare victims' teeth to records kept by dentists. They also use fingerprints, scars and other markings to identify victims.

Firefighters at the scene of the Argentine airliner that crashed during takeoff from Buenos Aires airport in 1999.

'The plane passed right in front of [our car] . . . the wing must have been a metre away. I could see the passengers through the plane's windows and I thought how horrible it must have been for them.'

– an eyewitness to the crash of an Argentine airliner in 1999

Firemen try to put out the smoke and flames of
the crashed Concorde in Paris.

2000

THE CONCORDE

For more than twenty-five years, the Concorde was the world's most famous passenger aeroplane. Most jetliners fly at about 885 kph (550 mph). The Concorde cruised at about 2,170 kph (1,350 mph). It was the only passenger plane that could fly faster than the speed of sound. (Sound travels at 1,062 kph or 660 mph.)

The Concorde whisked passengers between New York City and Paris in three and a half hours. That was twice as fast as other jetliners could make the trip. Two airlines, Air France and British Airways, began flying Concordes in 1976.

On 25 July 2000, pilot Christian Marty and co-pilot Jean Marcot were preparing to fly a Concorde from Paris to New York City. The flight was Air France Flight 4590. It had 109 people on board. The Concorde's engines roared, and Flight 4590 rolled down the runway at Charles de

Gaulle Airport in Paris. It gained just enough speed to lift off the ground. Then witnesses saw a startling sight: flames began trailing from the low-flying aircraft.

Pilot Sid Hare, was one eyewitness. *'I knew [the aeroplane] was in trouble,'* Hare said. *'It was trailing flames, 200 to 300 feet [60 to 90 m] behind the aeroplane. And it just couldn't gain altitude.'* Another witness, Frederic Savery, was driving home when the burning plane passed over his car. *'The whole back end of the plane was on fire,'* he said.

The Concorde crashed into a hotel. *'When it hit, there was just a huge fireball, like a mini-atomic bomb went up, and it was really just a sickening sight,'* said Sid Hare. All 109 people on the plane and 4 people on the ground died.

What had caused the disaster? A sharp piece of metal had broken off another plane and fallen onto the runway. One of the Concorde's tyres hit the metal and blew out. Pieces of the tyre punctured the plane's fuel tanks. The fuel caught on fire.

After the crash, designers gave the Concorde stronger tyres and fuel tanks, but people were afraid to fly on the plane. Within three years, Air France and British Airways decided to stop flying the Concorde.

'Concorde . . . you have flames! You have flames behind you!'

– an air traffic controller speaking to the Concorde pilots via radio

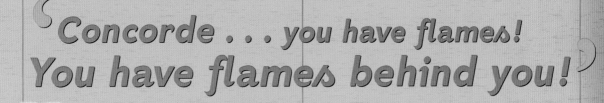

{ The Concorde trailed flames as it attempted to take off in Paris.

Getting Help—FAST

AIR DISASTERS USUALLY INVOLVE MANY DEATHS. WHEN AN AEROPLANE HITS THE GROUND, IT BREAKS INTO THOUSANDS OF PIECES. FLYING PIECES OF METAL CAN CUT, TRAP AND SMASH PASSENGERS. AEROPLANES ALSO CARRY LARGE AMOUNTS OF FUEL. WHEN A PLANE BREAKS APART, THAT FUEL SPILLS OUT. HEAT AND SPARKS FROM THE CRASH CAN SET THE FUEL ON FIRE. EVEN PEOPLE WHO LIVE THROUGH THE CRASH MAY BURN TO DEATH IN THE FIRE. MANY PARTS OF AN AEROPLANE, SUCH AS THE SEATS, WALLS AND STORAGE BINS, ARE MADE OF PLASTIC. WHEN PLASTIC BURNS, IT GIVES OFF POISONOUS SMOKE. PASSENGERS TRAPPED IN A BURNING PLANE MAY DIE FROM INHALING THE SMOKE.

Many people survive air disasters. Some survive because of good luck. Others survive because of aeroplane safety features, quick thinking on the part of flight crews and the quick response of emergency medical teams.

FIRST RESPONDERS

Aeroplane flight crews are trained to handle emergencies. Before take-off, flight crews give passengers a quick lesson on emergency procedures. They show passengers the plane's emergency exits, or extra doors. They tell passengers the importance of wearing seatbelts. In the first seconds after a crash, flight crews are the first rescue squads. They help passengers get out of the plane quickly.

Firefighters rescue an injured passenger after a plane crash in Costa Rica in 2000.

Large passenger aeroplanes have eight emergency exits. Emergency exits allow many people to leave an aeroplane at once. Passengers don't all have to file through a single door at the front of the plane. To help passengers reach the ground, emergency exits have slides. These slides are inflatable – they blow up like balloons. Passengers slide down these chutes to reach the ground safely.

A SUCCESS STORY

The story of Air France Flight 358 proves that air disasters don't have to be tragedies. The plane crashed upon landing at Toronto Pearson International Airport in Toronto, Canada. It began to burn. The plane carried 309 passengers. However, nobody died during the crash. Only forty-three people suffered injuries. The passengers and crew all survived because they got out of the aeroplane quickly.

The crew worked fast after the crash. 'People were tripping over each other, climbing over the seats to get to the exit,' said Dominique Pajot, a passenger on the flight. 'They [the flight crew] were very quick to get up and open the [emergency] doors and help people and calm them.' The flight crew's good work saved many lives.

Passengers of Air France Flight 358 run from the burning plane after it crashed upon landing in Toronto, Canada.

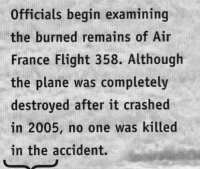

Officials begin examining the burned remains of Air France Flight 358. Although the plane was completely destroyed after it crashed in 2005, no one was killed in the accident.

'*It's nothing short of a miracle.*'

— Jean Lapierre, Canada's transport minister, remarking on Flight 358's 100 per cent survival rate

TO THE RESCUE

After an aeroplane crash, every second counts. Fire engines and rescue workers must arrive very quickly to help victims. Sometimes, if a pilot knows the plane is in trouble during flight, the pilot will notify the nearest airport. The airport will send out a rescue team even before the disaster happens. Large airports have their own fire engines and rescue teams. Airports sometimes ask for help from fire and medical workers in nearby cities.

Getting help fast can be difficult, however. Not all crashes occur near airports or cities. Some disasters happen over the sea or another body of water. Some disasters happen in wilderness areas with very few people. When a plane crashes in a remote area, rescue workers might have to use boats, helicopters or other special vehicles to reach the victims.

In 2006 an Armenian airliner crashed into the Black Sea, near Russia. Rescue workers travelled to the crash site in boats. But by the time they arrived, they found only dead bodies floating in the water. JAL Flight 123 crashed high in the mountains. It took rescuers twelve hours to reach the crash scene. By then many people who survived the crash had frozen to death.

EMOTIONAL SCARS

Long after an air disaster, the emotional scars remain. Those who lose friends and family members in a crash feel great sadness and shock. Those who survive a crash are often haunted by memories of the terrible event. Survivors who are injured must cope with health problems.

Several organizations, such as the Red Cross, specialize in helping disaster victims cope with their problems. These groups hire social workers and counsellors to offer support to victims and their families. Rescue workers often see horrible injuries and deaths at crash sites. Even they sometimes need counselling after air disasters.

This group of crash survivors waited for seventy days in the Andes Mountains of South America to be rescued. Two of the survivors walked down from the mountain to get help for the rest of the survivors.

Victims' families cope with their losses in different ways. Some start memorial funds named for their loved ones who died. Family, friends and others can contribute money to the funds. The money is used for good causes, such as helping students pay for education. These programmes give people a way to remember and honour those who died. Creating something positive from a tragedy helps survivors feel better.

After the 11 September air disasters, people around the world built monuments to honour the victims. New York City will have the biggest monument. It will cost more than $500 million to build. It will stand at the World Trade Center site. The monument, called Reflecting Absence, will include reflecting pools, a waterfall, a museum and a wall with the names of 11 September victims. New York has also started work on a new skyscraper, Freedom Tower, to replace the World Trade Center buildings. Reflecting Absence is scheduled to open in 2009, and Freedom Tower is set to open in 2011.

WONDER GIRL

Juliane Koepcke, a seventeen-year-old from Peru, sat next to her mother in an aeroplane in 1971. The plane flew through a thunderstorm over the rainforest in Peru. Juliane looked out of the window. She saw that the plane's wing was on fire. The last thing she remembered was spinning and falling through the air. Three hours later, she awoke in the rainforest. She had fallen 3.2 km (2 miles) to the ground. All the other ninety-one people on board the plane had died. How had Juliane survived? Winds in the thunderstorm may have blown upwards, slowing and cushioning her fall to the ground. Juliane wandered through the rainforest for eleven days before being rescued.

This simple but personal memorial stands in
the Pennsylvania field where United Flight 93
crashed on 11 September 2001.

This dramatic photograph shows the area of the Pentagon where American Flight 77 crashed into it on 11 September 2001.

11 SEPTEMBER 2001

On the morning of 11 September 2001, four aeroplanes were flying passengers to California. American Airlines Flight 11 and United Airlines Flight 175 had taken off from Boston. American Airlines Flight 77 had taken off from Virginia and United Airlines Flight 93 had taken off from New Jersey. Altogether, the planes carried 259 people.

Unknown to the crew and passengers, teams of terrorists were travelling on board each plane. After take-off, the terrorists hijacked (took control of) the aeroplanes.

The terrorists crashed United Flight 175 and American Flight 11 into the 110-storey World Trade Center in New York City. That famous skyscraper had twin towers rising 416 m into the air. More than fifty thousand people worked in the offices inside. About

48

two hundred thousand other people visited the buildings every day.

When the planes hit the towers, the fuel inside the aeroplanes exploded and caught fire. Hundreds of people inside the buildings died instantly. As the buildings burned, many people escaped by walking down stairways. Others were trapped by the fire. Rather than burn to death, some jumped out of windows high above the ground, even though they knew they would not survive the fall.

The burning fuel melted the steel columns that held up the buildings' floors. The floors fell one on top of another. As millions of people watched on live TV, both towers collapsed into a heap of wreckage. The wreckage buried people still trapped in the buildings. It also buried firefighters and police officers who were trying to rescue people.

Less than an hour after planes hit the World Trade Center, hijackers crashed American Flight 77 into the Pentagon near Washington, DC. This huge building is the headquarters of the US military. The crash set the Pentagon on fire. Everyone on the plane died. People working inside the Pentagon died too.

On United Flight 93, terrorists steered the plane towards Washington, DC. They probably planned to crash into the US Capitol building or the White House, but passengers decided to fight the hijackers. **'Are you guys ready?'** passenger Todd Beamer asked the other passengers as they prepared to fight. **'Let's roll!'** As the passengers struggled against the hijackers, the plane went down. It crashed in a field in Pennsylvania. Everyone on board died.

'*Everyone was screaming, crying, running, cops, people, firefighters, everyone. It's like a war zone.*'

– New York City firefighter Mike Smith, describing the World Trade Center attacks

The 11 September attacks killed about three thousand people. The attacks shocked and saddened people worldwide. After the attacks, the United States made many changes to air transport. It created the Transportation Security Administration. This government agency works to keep flights safe from terrorists and other dangers.

The Future

AIR DISASTERS ARE TERRIBLE. HOWEVER, THEY ALSO TEACH US LESSONS THAT CAN MAKE FLYING SAFER. FOR INSTANCE, AFTER THE 1956 GRAND CANYON AIR DISASTER, THE US GOVERNMENT STARTED A NEW AIR SAFETY OFFICE. THAT OFFICE BECAME THE MODERN-DAY FEDERAL AVIATION ADMINISTRATION.

Modern air travel is very safe, and it is likely to get even safer. That's because aeroplane designers are always looking for ways to improve aeroplanes and their safety equipment.

WIRELESS BLACK BOXES

In the future, aeroplanes might use wireless technology instead of flight data recorders and cockpit voice recorders. With 'wireless black boxes,' aeroplanes will not store data on board. Instead, cockpit voice recordings and other data will travel in real time (second by second) to stations on the ground. Ground stations will record and save the information. It will always be available – fast – in case of a disaster. No one will have to search for a black box at a crash site.

Wireless technology will also help pilots to cope when disasters threaten. Imagine if JAL Flight 123 had had wireless technology before its tail fin broke off. A wireless black box could have warned airline mechanics on the ground that the tail was getting dangerously weak. The mechanics could have told the pilots to land before the tail broke off.

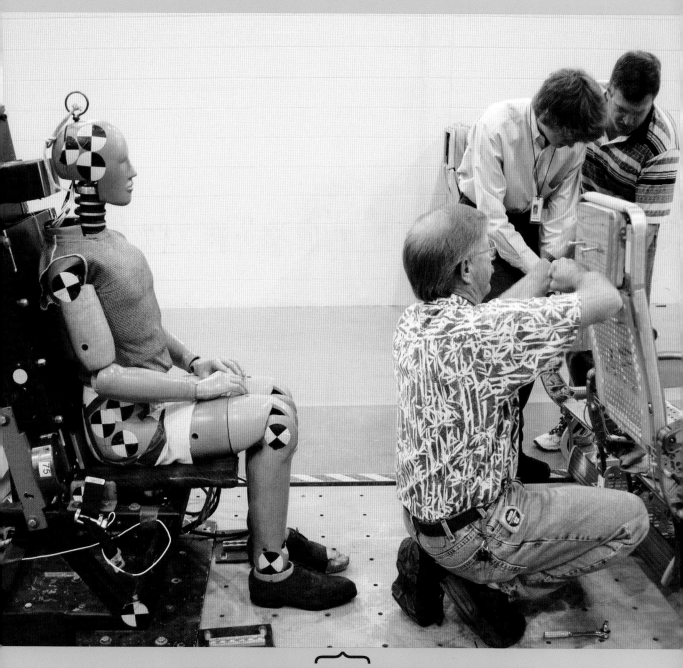

Officials use a crash test dummy to test airline seat
safety at the Federal Aviation Administration training
and research facility in Oklahoma City, Oklahoma, USA.

FIREPROOF FUEL

Many passengers survive an aeroplane crash at first, but then they die in the fire caused by spilled fuel. In the future, aeroplanes may use fuel that doesn't catch fire easily after a crash. Some military aircraft already use this kind of fuel. This fuel is more expensive than regular fuel, so if passenger airlines use it, they will have to charge passengers more for tickets.

EMPTYING THE SKIES

After the four planes crashed on 11 September, nobody knew if terrorists might be on board other aeroplanes. For safety, the US government grounded all non-military aeroplanes in the United States. About forty-five hundred aeroplanes were already in the air at the time of the disasters. All those planes had to land at the nearest airport.

FIGHTING SMOKE

After an aeroplane crash, a plane usually catches on fire. Thick smoke fills the plane. Crash survivors often cannot see exit doors through the smoke. Adding to the danger, people breathe in deadly smoke from burning plastic inside the plane. In the future, aeroplanes may be built with safer plastics. These new plastics will not burn or will burn very slowly, giving people more time to escape after a crash. In addition, the plastics will not release poisonous gases when they are burned.

Planes in the future may also be equipped with a smoke hood for each passenger. A smoke hood is a clear plastic bag with an air filter. The hood fits over a passenger's head. It protects the face and hair from fire and also filters out toxic gases. After a crash, smoke hoods would help passengers escape a burning plane.

Flames and smoke engulfed this Boeing 737 after it crash-landed in Indonesia in March 2007. In the future, changes in the design of planes will make them less likely to burn and create dangerous smoke when they crash.

PARACHUTES FOR PASSENGERS

When military planes fall
out of the sky, the pilots
have one last chance to
survive. They can leave
the plane using a device
called an ejection seat. An
ejection seat sends a pilot
rocketing out of a doomed plane.
The pilot then floats to the ground
using a parachute. Why can't airline
passengers also escape by parachute? In
the future, they may do so.

In the future, aeroplane
passengers might have
parachutes to use in
escaping a crash.

However, parachuting for passengers
won't be easy. Using a parachute safely takes
a great deal of training. Most passengers do
not have that training. So engineers must work
out how to make parachuting safe for untrained
people.

FEAR-FREE FLYING

As terrible as air disasters are, remember that they are extremely rare.
Don't let worries about air disasters spoil the fun of flying. Always
remember that flying is the safest kind of travel.

AIR TRAVEL SAFETY TIPS

By following a few safety tips, you can make your next aeroplane ride even safer. To improve your safety:

• Listen to the pre-flight safety instructions. During these instructions, flight attendants will tell you what to do in an emergency. Listen to the instructions every time you fly, even if you have heard them before.

• Locate the emergency exits on your plane. Think about how you would reach the nearest exit in an emergency.

• Keep your seatbelt on throughout the flight. With your seatbelt fastened, you will stay safely in your seat if the flight suddenly becomes rough.

• In an emergency, follow instructions from the flight attendants, who are trained to deal with emergencies. Do exactly as they say.

• Think quickly after a crash. Unfasten your seatbelt and get out of the plane as fast as you can.

• Fly in large aeroplanes instead of small ones when possible. Your chances of surviving an air disaster are better in a large plane than in a small one. Large planes have more metal to protect passengers from the force of a crash.

Timeline

1903 Wilbur and Orville Wright make the first successful aeroplane flight at Kitty Hawk, North Carolina, USA (below).

1908 Thomas Selfridge, flying with Orville Wright, becomes the first person to die in an aeroplane crash.

1937 The Hindenburg crashes in Lakehurst, New Jersey.

1956 Two planes collide over the Grand Canyon, killing all 128 people on board.

1974 A cargo door on a Turkish aeroplane is not closed properly before take-off. The error causes the plane to crash, killing 346 people.

1977 Two planes collide on a runway in the Canary Islands, killing 583 people.

1979 An engine falls from an American Airlines flight in Chicago (left). The plane crashes, killing 273 people. Air New Zealand Flight 901 crashes into Mount Erebus in Antarctica, killing 257 people.

1983 A South Korean airliner flies off course into the Soviet Union. Soviet fighter jets shoot down the aeroplane, killing all 269 people aboard.

1985 Japan Airlines Flight 123 crashes in the mountains in Japan, killing 520 people.

1988 A US Navy ship shoots down an Iranian aeroplane. More than 300 people die in the crash. Libyan terrorists plant a bomb on Pan American Flight 103. The plane explodes over Lockerbie, Scotland, killing 270 people.

1994 American Eagle Flight 4184 flies into freezing rain in Indiana. The plane crashes, killing all 68 people on board.

1996 A pilot on a Kazakhstani aeroplane misunderstands air traffic control instructions. The plane collides with a Saudi Arabian aeroplane over India (left). The crash kills 351 people.

1998 Swissair Flight 111 crashes near Nova Scotia, Canada, killing 229 people.

2001 Terrorists crash four aeroplanes in the United States on 11 September. The crashes kill around 3,000 people. American Airlines Flight 587 crashes into a neighbourhood in Rockaway Beach, New York. The crash kills all 260 people on board and 5 people on the ground.

2005 During a snowstorm in Chicago, Southwest Airlines Flight 1248 skids upon landing. The plane crashes into several cars (above), killing a six-year-old boy.

2006 An Armenian airliner crashes into the Black Sea near Russia, killing 113 people.

2007 A Brazilian airliner skids off the runway and hits a building in San Paolo, Brazil (left). The crash kills 187 people on the plane and 12 people on the ground.

Glossary

aircraft: vehicles that fly through the air, such as aeroplanes, helicopters and airships

Air Accidents Investigation Branch (AAIB): a UK government body that studies aeroplane and other transport accidents. The AAIB also looks for ways to make transport systems safer.

altitude: height above the ground

black boxes: devices on board aeroplanes that record pilots' voices and data such as speed, direction and altitude

Civil Aviation Authority: the UK government body responsible for aeroplane safety

cockpit: the compartment inside an aeroplane where the pilots sit and control the plane

control tower: a tall building at an airport where workers give take-off and landing instructions to pilots and track planes with radar and other devices

cruising: the middle part of an aeroplane flight, when a plane is flying straight through the sky at a high altitude

de-icing: spraying aeroplanes with a chemical that melts snow and ice on wings

glide: to descend gradually in an aircraft

microbursts: small, strong gusts of wind that can swipe an aeroplane out of the sky

radar: a device that uses radio waves to detect and locate objects, such as planes and storm clouds

turbulence: sudden changes in the wind that can shake up an aeroplane in flight

Places to Visit

National Museum of Flight, Scotland
http://www.nms.ac.uk/museumofflighthome-
page.aspx
This museum explores the history of humankind's
quest to travel into the skies. With exhibitions
ranging from pioneer aircraft of the 1800s to
modern day jets and missiles.

Royal Air Force Museum, London
http://www.rafmuseum.org.uk/london/index.cfm
London's RAF museum has a huge collection of
historic and modern military aircraft.

Source Notes

4 Lee Gaillard, 'Composites at the Tip of the
Iceberg,' *Aviation Today Special Reports*, 4 May 2006,
http://www.aviationtoday.com/reports/iceberg.htm
(15 April 2006).

4 William Lucia, 'American Flight 587 Crashes into
Residential Queens; 260 Dead,' *Washington Square
News*, 13 November 2001, http://www.uwire
.com/content/topnews111301002.html (6 April
2006).

4 Ibid.

5 Ibid.

5 Jason Carroll, 'Crash Scene Already Scarred by
September Attacks, *CNN.com*, 12 November
2001, http://archives.cnn.com/2001/US/11/12/
newyork.crash.scene (6 April 2006).

9 Airliners.net, 'Dutch Jet Plummets,' *Airliners.net*, 15
December 1989, http://www1.airliners.net/
discussions/general_aviation/read.main/2550162/
?searchid=2550162&s=david+farrell#ID2550162
(19 November, 2006).

11 Malcolm MacPherson, ed., *On a Wing and a Prayer:
Interviews with Airline Disaster Survivors* (New York:
HarperCollins, 2002), 182.

12 Rick Archbold, *Hindenburg: An Illustrated History*
(Toronto: Warner / Madison Press, 1994), 162.

13 Jay Robert Nash, *Darkest Hours* (Chicago: Nelson-
Hall, 1976), 240.

13 Stephen J. Spignesi, *The 100 Greatest Disasters of All
Time* (New York: Kensington Publishing Corp.,
2002), 288.

13 Nash, *Darkest Hours*, 243.

13 Spignesi, *The 100 Greatest Disasters*, 288.

15 *USA Today*, 'At Least 121 Killed in South Korea Plane Crash,' *USAToday.com*, 15 April 2002, http://www.usatoday.com/news/world/2002/04/15/south-korea-plane-crash.htm (16 August, 2007).

21 William Bartomeu, 'Eyewitness Report: Fine Air Flight 101, *AirDisaster.com*, n.d., http://airdisaster.com/eyewitness/fine101.shtml (1 May 2006).

25 *Arizona Aircraft Archaeology*, 'TWA and United Collision over Grand Canyon,' 2003, http://www.aircraftarchaeology.com/twa_united_airlines_grand_canyon.htm (7 May 2006).

27 Parker Moon, 'Eyewitness Report: Southwest Airlines 1455,' *AirDisaster.com*, n.d., http://airdisaster.com/eyewitness/wn1455.shtml (1 May 2006).

31 David M. Lisk, comp., 'SkyNet – Special Report,' *Airline Disasters 1920–1997*, 1997, http://dnausers.d-n-a.net/dnetGOJG/120885.htm (6 April, 2006).

31 Ed Magnuson, 'Last Minutes of JAL 123,' *Time.com*, 21 June 2005, http://www.time.com/time/magazine/article/0,9171,1074738-7.00.html (19 November 2006).

31 Ibid.

31 Ibid.

37 Gilbert LeGras, 'At Least 63 Confirmed Dead in Buenos Aires Air Crash,' *Accident Reconstruction.com*, 1 September 1999, http://www.accidentreconstruction.com/news/sep99/090199c.html (27 February 2006).

39 BBC, 'Witnesses Describe Concorde Fireball,' *BBC.com*, 25 July 2005, http://new.bbc.co.uk/1/hi/world/europe/851250.stm (8 May 2006).

39 Ibid.

39 Ibid.

39 BBC, 'Transcript: The Crew's Last Words,' *BBC.com*, 31 August 2000, http://news.bbc.co.uk/1/hi/world/europe/905308.stm (8 May 2006).

42 Beth Duff-Brown, Associated Press, 'Canada Plane Crash Has Textbook Evacuation,' 3 August 2005, 1.

43 Duff-Brown, 'Canada Plane Crash.'

49 Jim McKinnon, 'The Phone Line from Flight 93 Was Still Open When a GTE Operator Heard Todd Beamer Say: 'Are you guys ready? Let's roll,'' *Pittsburgh Post-Gazette*, 16 September 2001, http://www.post-gazette.com/headlines/20010916phonecallnat3p3.asp (22 October 2006).

49 Guardian, 'Special Report: 11 September 2001,' *Guardian Unlimited*, 12 September 2001, http://www.guardian.co.uk/september11/story/0,,600839,00.html (15 April 2006).

Selected Bibliography

Adair, Bill. *The Mystery of Flight 427: Inside a Crash Investigation*. Washington, DC: Smithsonian Institution Press, 2002.

American Red Cross. 'Aviation Disasters: Unique Disasters Demand Unique Responses.' 2002. http://www.redcross.org/news/ds/trans/030115Airteam.html (15 April 2006).

Aviation Internet Group. *Aviation History On-Line Museum*. 8 April 2006. http://www.aviation-history.com/ (29 April 2006).

Bilstein, Roger E. *Flight in America: From the Wrights to the Astronauts*. Baltimore: Johns Hopkins University Press, 1984.

Blatner, David. *The Flying Book: Everything You've Ever Wondered about Flying on Airplanes*. New York: Walker & Co., 2003.

Boetius, Henning. *The Phoenix: A Novel about the Hindenburg*. New York: N. A. Talese, 2001.

Davis, Lee. *Man Made Disasters*. New York: Facts on File, 2002.

Department of Transportation. 10 January 2006. http://www.dot.gov/ (3 April 2006).

Federal Aviation Administration. 25 March 2006. http://www.faa.gov/ (25 April 2006).

First Flight Society. 'Lieutenant Thomas E. Selfridge.' *First Flight Society*. 2006. http://www.firstflight.org/shrine/thomas_selfridge.cfm (3 April 2006).

Job, Macarthur, and Matthew Tesch. *Air Disaster*. Vol. 2. Fyshwick, AU: Australian Aviation, 1996.

MacPherson, Malcolm, ed. *On a Wing and a Prayer: Interviews with Airline Disaster Survivors*. New York: HarperCollins, 2002.

Mooney, Michael M. *The Hindenburg*. New York: Dodd, Mead & Company, 1972.

National Transportation Safety Board. 2006. http://www.ntsb.gov/ (3 April 2006).

Negroni, Christine. *Deadly Departure*. New York: Cliff Street Books, 2000.

Rinard, Judith E. *The Story of Flight: The Smithsonian National Air and Space Museum*. Buffalo: Firefly Books, 2002.

Spignesi, Stephen J. *The 100 Greatest Disasters of All Time*. New York: Kensington Publishing Corp., 2002.

Winter, Frank H., and F. Robert van der Linden. *100 Years of Flight: A Chronicle of Aerospace History, 1903–2003*. Reston, VA: American Institute of Aeronautics and Astronautics, 2003.

Further Resources

BOOKS

Deary, Terry. *Terry Deary's Terribly True Disaster Stories* (Terry Deary's Terribly True Stories) Scholastic, 2006.

Flying Machines (Eyewitness) Dorling Kindersley Publishers Limited, 2003.

Gifford, Clive. *Planes and Helicopters* (Usborne Big Machines) Usborne Publishing Limited, 2004.

Hughes, Monica. *Jumbo Jet Pilot:* Fact Monsters Ticktock Media, 2008.

MacDonald, Fiona. *The September 11th Terrorist Attacks* (Days That Changed the World) World Almanac Library, 2004.

Mark Jan and Alex Pang. *Aeroplanes* Oxford University Press, 2003.

Oxlade, Chris. *Planes* (Transport Around the World) Heinemann Library, 2007.

Patchett, Fiona. *Planes* (Usborne Beginners)Usborne Publishing Ltd, 2007.

Platt, Richard, *Flight* (Dorling Kindersley Experience) Dorling Kindersley Publishers Limited, 2006.

Rohr, Ian. *Transport Planes* (Go Facts) A & C Black Publishers Limited, 2006.

WEBSITES AND FILMS

BBC News – Air Disasters Timeline
http://news.bbc.co.uk/1/hi/in_depth/2008892.stm
Read about air disasters that have happened in recent years.

National Flight Museum (Scotland) – Plane Builder
http://www.nms.ac.uk/planebuilder.aspx
In this game you must choose the parts to build your own plane to escape from the jungle. Will you make it out alive?

Royal Air Force
http://www.raf.mod.uk/
Learn about the UK's air force. This website includes a history of the RAF and a section which explains the different types of planes and equipment that they use.

Science Museum – Transport
http://www.sciencemuseum.org.uk/onlinestuff/subjects/transport.aspx
Look on this website to find out more about planes. It includes sections on advancements in aviation, the Spitfire fighter plane and the first female pilot to fly solo to Australia from Britain.

Index

aeroplanes: first crash victim 10; flight stages 26; flying height 18; history of 10; statistics for 8

Airbus A380 6

Air Accidents Investigations Branch (AAIB) 32, 34, 36

Air China Flight 129 14

Air Florida Flight 90 20

Air France Flight 358 42; Flight 4590 38

Air New Zealand Flight 901 16

air traffic controllers 16

air turbulence 20

airship 12, 13

Aloha Airlines Flight 243 11

American Airlines: Flight 11 48; Flight 77 48; Flight 587 4

American Eagle Flight 4184 20

Atlantic Ocean 22, 36

black boxes 32, 34, 36, 50

blimp 12, 13. See also airship

Boeing 747 4, 6, 26–27, 30

Charles de Gaulle Airport 38

Civil Aviation Authority 10

Concorde 38–39

crashes: causes 14, 16, 18, 20, 22; investigations of 32, 34, 36; map of 28

CVR (cockpit voice recorder) 34. See also black boxes

Eastern Airlines Flight 401, 34

emergency exits 42

Ethiopian Airlines 22

eyewitness accounts 4, 5, 9, 13, 15, 21, 27, 30–31, 39, 42, 49

FDR (flight data recorder) 34. See also black boxes

flight crews 40, 42

Freedom Tower 46

future technology 50, 52, 54

Gandy, Jack 25. See also United Airlines: Flight 718

Grand Canyon, AZ 24–25

Hindenburg 12, 13. See also airship

identifying victims 36

JAL (Japan Airlines) Flight 123 30, 50

John F Kennedy International Airport 4

Kitty Hawk, NC 10

landing 27

Lockerbie, Scotland 9

Marcot, Jean 38. See also Concorde

microbursts 20

New York City, NY 4, 6, 46, 48

Pan American Flight 103 9

Pennsylvania 6, 47, 49

Pentagon 6, 49

pilot training 14

Reflecting Absence 46

Rockaway Beach, NY 4

safety 8, 10, 26, 40, 42; tips 55

September 11, 2001 6, 46, 48–49

Southwest Airlines: Flight 1248 18; Flight 1445, 27

tail fin 4, 30–31

Takahama, Masami 31. See also JAL (Japan Airlines) Flight 123

take-off 26–27

terrorism 9, 14, 48

Toronto Pearson International Airport 42

Transportation Security Administration 49

TWA (Trans World Airlines): Flight 2, 24, 25; Flight 800 22, 36

United Airlines: Flight 93 48–49; Flight 175 48; Flight 718 24, 25

wake turbulence 4

Washington, DC 6, 49

World Trade Center 6, 46, 48

Wright brothers 10. See also aeroplanes: history of

Photo Acknowledgements

The images in this book are used with the permission of: © Bryn Colton/Assignments Photographers/CORBIS, p 1; © Central Press/Hulton Archive/Getty Images, p 3; © Chris Gardner/AFP/Getty Images, p 5; © Jochen Guenther/AFP/Getty Images, p 6; © CNN via Getty Images, p 7; © Hudson-Langevin-Nogues/Sygma/CORBIS, p 9; Library of Congress, pp 10 (LC-USZ61-473), 56 (top) (LC-DIG-ppprs-00626); © Tim Bieber/Stone/Getty Images, p 11; © Hulton Archive/Getty Images, p 12; © Mansell/Time & Life Pictures/Getty Images, p 13; © Daniel Esgro Photography/Riser/Getty Images, p 14; © Lee Jae-Chan/Getty Images, p 15; © Gary Williams/Getty Images, p 16; © Paul Chesley/Stone/Getty Images, p 17; © Ipung/EPA/CORBIS, pp 19 (background), 53; © Bill Hauser/Independent Picture Service, pp 19, 28-29; © Thomas Cooper/Getty Images, p 20; © Terry Ashe/Time & Life Pictures/Getty Images, p 21; © Arthur Morris/Visuals Unlimited, Inc, p 22; © Robert Sagliocca/FBI/Time & Life Pictures/Getty Images, p 23; © Bettmann/CORBIS, pp 24, 56 (bottom); © Carl Iwasaki/Time & Life Pictures/Getty Images, p 25; © Chris Martinez/Getty Images, p 27; AP Photo, p 30; © STR/AFP/Getty Images, p 31; © Reuters/CORBIS, pp 33, 41 © Jon Levy/AFP/Getty Images, p 35; AP Photo/Pablo Vernengo, p 37; AP Photo/Joachim Bertrand/Ministry of Interior/Civil Security, File, p 38; AP Photo/Toshihiko Sato, p 39; © Eddie Ho/Toronto Star/ZUMA Press, p 42; © Frank Gunn/AFP/Getty Images, p 43; © Group of Survivors/CORBIS, p 45; © Jeff Swensen/Getty Images, p 47; Cedric H. Rudisill/United States Department of Defense, p 48; © Benjamin Lowry/CORBIS, p 51; © David McNew/Getty Images, p 54; AP Photo/Jack Dempsey, p 55 (background); © Kapoor Baldev/Sygma/CORBIS, p 57 (top); © Frank Polich/Reuters/CORBIS, p 57 (middle); © Eugenio Goulart/AFP/Getty Images, p 57 (bottom).

Front Cover: © Richard Kaylin/Stone/Getty Images.
Back Cover: © NYPD/Getty Images.

About the Authors

Michael Woods is a science and medical journalist in Washington, DC, USA, who has won many national writing awards. Mary B Woods is a school librarian. Their past books include the eight-volume Ancient Technology series. Michael and Mary have four children. When not writing, reading or enjoying their grandchildren, they travel to gather material for future books.

Text by Stella Gurney
Illustrations by Joel Stewart and Davide Arnone

First published 2013 by Walker Books Ltd
87 Vauxhall Walk, London SE11 5HJ

10 9 8 7 6 5 4 3 2 1

The Adventures of Abney & Teal © and ™ 2011 Ragdoll Worldwide Ltd.
Produced by Ragdoll.
Licensed by Ragdoll Worldwide Ltd.

This book has been typeset in AbneyandTeal font

Printed in China

British Library Cataloguing in Publication Data: a catalogue record
for this book is available from the British Library

ISBN 978-1-4063-4812-5
www.walker.co.uk